Y0-AGW-439

Dinosaurs In Space

A Book to Read and Color

Written and Illustrated by
Jill E. Osborne

Watermill Press

© 1985 by Watermill Press, Mahwah, N.J. All rights reserved.

Once upon a time,
three dinosaurs bought
a spaceship.

AL ALLOSAURUS'
USED
ROCKETS AND
SPACESHIPS

PRICE—10 ROCKS

They made their spaceship look like new.

Now they are ready to go!

Where will they go?

"I am the largest dinosaur here," Brontosaurus says.
"Let's go to the planet Jupiter."

"No, no," says Stegosaurus.
"We have never been to Saturn, so let's go there!"

"Wait a minute! Mars is my favorite planet,
so let's go there," says Triceratops.

"Hold it! Hold it!"
Stegosaurus says.

10

All is quiet.

"We have to be fair.
Let's draw a name out of a hat."

He picks Triceratops' name.
The dinosaurs are going to Mars!

They get into their spacesuits…

They get into their spaceship...

Off they go!

The spaceship flies by many stars.

Suddenly, there is Mars.

Mars is red, with white polar caps.
They look like they are made of ice.
There is no green in sight.
There is nothing to eat!

Mars

SHUTTLE

"Let's not stop at Mars,"
Triceratops says. "There are
no green plants to eat.
And I am getting hungry."

DINOSAUR

SHUTTLE

Next stop is Jupiter. It takes the dinosaurs a long, long time to get to Jupiter.

"When will we get there?" Brontosaurus asks.
"Now I am getting hungry, too."

Suddenly, there is Jupiter.

It is the biggest planet in our solar system. There is a thin ring around Jupiter. The planet is covered with different colored clouds. In the clouds is the Great Red Spot. The dinosaurs don't see any green plants to eat at all.

"Well, let's go to Saturn," says Stegosaurus. "Maybe we can eat and have fun there."

Off they go to Saturn!

SHUTTLE

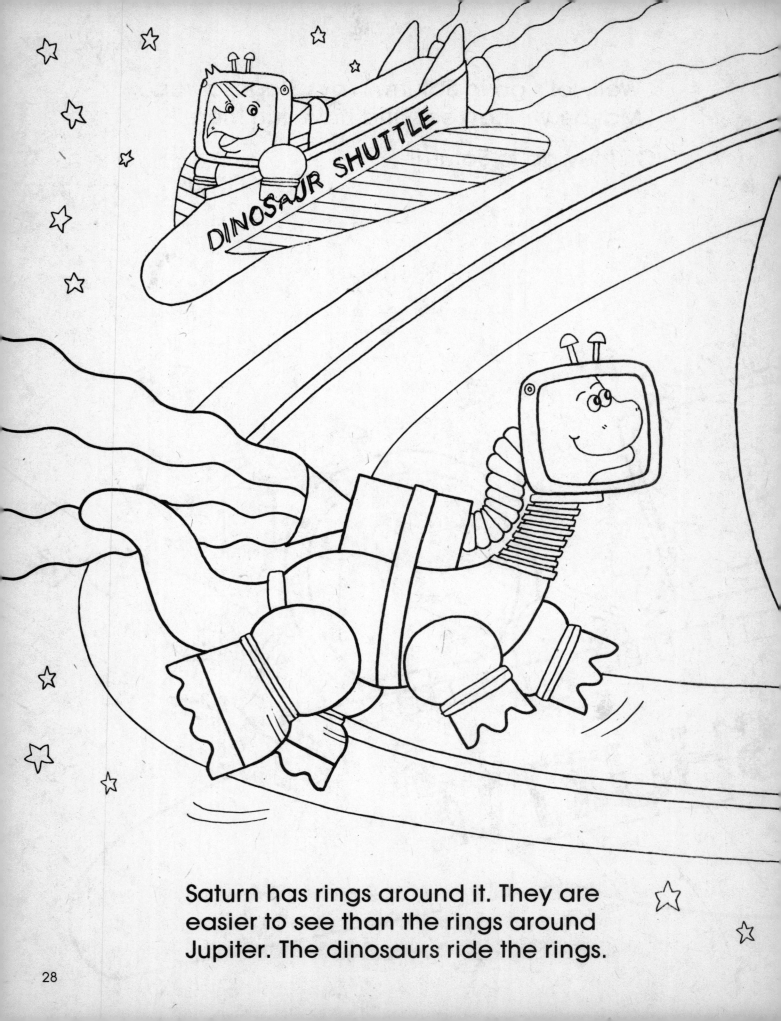

Saturn has rings around it. They are easier to see than the rings around Jupiter. The dinosaurs ride the rings.

"Wheeee! This is fun!" says Stegosaurus.
"But now I'm really hungry!"
What should they do?

"Let's go home to our trees and plants and friends,"
Brontosaurus says. "Let's go home to Earth."

The dinosaurs hurry home in their spaceship.

Hooray for Earth!
Earth is the planet they like best!